Wendy
ope
amily
alues

Walter
de la Mare
Selected
Poems
Edited by Matthew Sweeney

ff   Poetry

Poems
Edited by Peter Porter

ff   Poetry

MW00365598

Tulips
Poems 1968–2011

ff   Poetry

avid
arsent
ight

Michael
Hofmann
Selected
Poems

ff   Poetry

Mick Imlah
The Lost
Leader

ff   Poetry

Emma Jones
The Striped
World

ff   Poetry

Paul
Muldoon
Maggot

Poetry   ff

Daljit Nagra
Tippoo Sultan's
Incredible
White-Man-
Eating Tiger
Toy-Machine!!!

Poetry   ff

Alice
Oswald
Memorial

Poetry   ff

Don
Paterson
Rain

Poetry   ff

Jo
Shapcott
Of
Mutability

Stephen
Spender
New
Collected
Poems

Poetry   ff

Derek
Walcott
White
Egrets

Poetry   ff

Hugo
Williams
West End
Final

Poetry   ff

Faber & Faber

Poetry Diary 2020

Faber & Faber was founded in 1929 ...

... but its roots go back further to the Scientific Press, which started publishing in the early years of the century. The press's largest shareholders were Sir Maurice and Lady Gwyer, and their desire to expand into general publishing led them to Geoffrey Faber, a fellow of All Souls College, Oxford. Faber and Gwyer was founded in 1925. After four years Faber took the company forward alone, and the story goes that Walter de la Mare suggested adding a second, fictitious Faber to balance the company name.

In the meantime, the firm had prospered. T. S. Eliot, who had been suggested to Geoffrey Faber by a colleague at All Souls, had left Lloyds Bank in London to join him as a director, and in its first season the firm issued Eliot's *Poems 1909–1925*. In addition, the catalogues from the early years included books by Jean Cocteau, Herbert Read and Vita Sackville-West.

Poetry was always to be a significant element in the list and under Eliot's aegis Marianne Moore, Louis MacNeice and David Jones soon joined Ezra Pound, W. H. Auden, Stephen Spender, James Joyce, Siegfried Sassoon, D. H. Lawrence and Walter de la Mare.

Under Geoffrey Faber's chairmanship the board in 1929 included Eliot, Richard de la Mare, Charles Stewart and Frank Morley. This young team built up a comprehensive and profitable catalogue distinguished by modern design, much of which is still in print. Biographies, memoirs, fiction, poetry, political and religious essays, art and architecture monographs, children's books and a pioneering range of ecology titles contributed towards an eclectic list full of character. Faber also produced Eliot's groundbreaking literary review *The Criterion*.

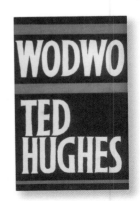

The Second World War brought both paper shortages and higher taxes, and the post-war years continued to be difficult. However, as the economy recovered a new generation of writers joined Faber, including William Golding, Robert Lowell, Ted Hughes, Sylvia Plath, Seamus Heaney, Philip Larkin, Thom Gunn and P. D. James. The publishing of Samuel Beckett and John Osborne began the firm's commitment to a modern drama list that now includes Tom Stoppard, Harold Pinter and David Hare.

From the 1970s through to the 1990s there was a blossoming in literary fiction, with the addition of authors such as Peter Carey, Kazuo Ishiguro, Barbara Kingsolver, Milan Kundera, Mario Vargas Llosa and Orhan Pamuk.

The year 2020 finds the publishing company that Geoffrey Faber founded remaining true to the principles he instigated and independent of corporate ownership. In its ninety years of publishing, Faber & Faber can count among its authors seven Carnegie Medal winners, three Kate Greenaway Medal winners, more than twenty Whitbread/Costa Book Award winners, seven Man Booker Prize winners, twelve Forward Poetry Prize winners, and thirteen Nobel Laureates.

Death of a Naturalist

by Seamus Heaney

In addition to dedicated core publishing, recent years have seen some new strands emerge, including a distinctive Faber Audio list, the launch of the Faber Academy writing school and a Faber Members programme.

A more detailed chronology of Faber & Faber's poetry publishing appears at the back of this diary.

JANUARY

M	T	W	T	F	S	S
30	31	1	2	3	4	5
6	7	8	9	10	11	12
13	14	15	16	17	18	19
20	21	22	23	24	25	26
27	28	29	30	31	1	2
3	4	5	6	7	8	9

FEBRUARY

M	T	W	T	F	S	S
27	28	29	30	31	1	2
3	4	5	6	7	8	9
10	11	12	13	14	15	16
17	18	19	20	21	22	23
24	25	26	27	28	29	1
2	3	4	5	6	7	8

MARCH

M	T	W	T	F	S	S
24	25	26	27	28	29	1
2	3	4	5	6	7	8
9	10	11	12	13	14	15
16	17	18	19	20	21	22
23	24	25	26	27	28	29
30	31	1	2	3	4	5

APRIL

M	T	W	T	F	S	S
30	31	1	2	3	4	5
6	7	8	9	10	11	12
13	14	15	16	17	18	19
20	21	22	23	24	25	26
27	28	29	30	1	2	3
4	5	6	7	8	9	10

MAY

M	T	W	T	F	S	S
27	28	29	30	1	2	3
4	5	6	7	8	9	10
11	12	13	14	15	16	17
18	19	20	21	22	23	24
25	26	27	28	29	30	31
1	2	3	4	5	6	7

JUNE

M	T	W	T	F	S	S
1	2	3	4	5	6	7
8	9	10	11	12	13	14
15	16	17	18	19	20	21
22	23	24	25	26	27	28
29	30	1	2	3	4	5
6	7	8	9	10	11	12

JULY

M	T	W	T	F	S	S
29	30	1	2	3	4	5
6	7	8	9	10	11	12
13	14	15	16	17	18	19
20	21	22	23	24	25	26
27	28	29	30	31	1	2
3	4	5	6	7	8	9

AUGUST

M	T	W	T	F	S	S
27	28	29	30	31	1	2
3	4	5	6	7	8	9
10	11	12	13	14	15	16
17	18	19	20	21	22	23
24	25	26	27	28	29	30
31	1	2	3	4	5	6

SEPTEMBER

M	T	W	T	F	S	S
31	1	2	3	4	5	6
7	8	9	10	11	12	13
14	15	16	17	18	19	20
21	22	23	24	25	26	27
28	29	30	1	2	3	4
5	6	7	8	9	10	11

OCTOBER

M	T	W	T	F	S	S
28	29	30	1	2	3	4
5	6	7	8	9	10	11
12	13	14	15	16	17	18
19	20	21	22	23	24	25
26	27	28	29	30	31	1
2	3	4	5	6	7	8

NOVEMBER

M	T	W	T	F	S	S
26	27	28	29	30	31	1
2	3	4	5	6	7	8
9	10	11	12	13	14	15
16	17	18	19	20	21	22
23	24	25	26	27	28	29
30	1	2	3	4	5	6

DECEMBER

M	T	W	T	F	S	S
30	1	2	3	4	5	6
7	8	9	10	11	12	13
14	15	16	17	18	19	20
21	22	23	24	25	26	27
28	29	30	31	1	2	3
4	5	6	7	8	9	10

JANUARY

M	T	W	T	F	S	S
31	1	2	3	4	5	6
7	8	9	10	11	12	13
14	15	16	17	18	19	20
21	22	23	24	25	26	27
28	29	30	31	1	2	3
4	5	6	7	8	9	10

FEBRUARY

M	T	W	T	F	S	S
28	29	30	31	1	2	3
4	5	6	7	8	9	10
11	12	13	14	15	16	17
18	19	20	21	22	23	24
25	26	27	28	1	2	3
4	5	6	7	8	9	10

MARCH

M	T	W	T	F	S	S
25	26	27	28	1	2	3
4	5	6	7	8	9	10
11	12	13	14	15	16	17
18	19	20	21	22	23	24
25	26	27	28	29	30	31
1	2	3	4	5	6	7

APRIL

M	T	W	T	F	S	S
25	26	27	28	29	30	31
1	2	3	4	5	6	7
8	9	10	11	12	13	14
15	16	17	18	19	20	21
22	23	24	25	26	27	28
29	30	1	2	3	4	5

MAY

M	T	W	T	F	S	S
29	30	1	2	3	4	5
6	7	8	9	10	11	12
13	14	15	16	17	18	19
20	21	22	23	24	25	26
27	28	29	30	31	1	2
3	4	5	6	7	8	9

JUNE

M	T	W	T	F	S	S
27	28	29	30	31	1	2
3	4	5	6	7	8	9
10	11	12	13	14	15	16
17	18	19	20	21	22	23
24	25	26	27	28	29	30
1	2	3	4	5	6	7

JULY

M	T	W	T	F	S	S
24	25	26	27	28	29	30
1	2	3	4	5	6	7
8	9	10	11	12	13	14
15	16	17	18	19	20	21
22	23	24	25	26	27	28
29	30	31	1	2	3	4

AUGUST

M	T	W	T	F	S	S
29	30	31	1	2	3	4
5	6	7	8	9	10	11
12	13	14	15	16	17	18
19	20	21	22	23	24	25
26	27	28	29	30	31	1
2	3	4	5	6	7	8

SEPTEMBER

M	T	W	T	F	S	S
26	27	28	29	30	31	1
2	3	4	5	6	7	8
9	10	11	12	13	14	15
16	17	18	19	20	21	22
23	24	25	26	27	28	29
30	1	2	3	4	5	6

OCTOBER

M	T	W	T	F	S	S
30	1	2	3	4	5	6
7	8	9	10	11	12	13
14	15	16	17	18	19	20
21	22	23	24	25	26	27
28	29	30	31	1	2	3
4	5	6	7	8	9	10

NOVEMBER

M	T	W	T	F	S	S
28	29	30	31	1	2	3
4	5	6	7	8	9	10
11	12	13	14	15	16	17
18	19	20	21	22	23	24
25	26	27	28	29	30	1
2	3	4	5	6	7	8

DECEMBER

M	T	W	T	F	S	S
25	26	27	28	29	30	1
2	3	4	5	6	7	8
9	10	11	12	13	14	15
16	17	18	19	20	21	22
23	24	25	26	27	28	29
30	31	1	2	3	4	5

JANUARY

M	T	W	T	F	S	S
28	29	30	31	1	2	3
4	5	6	7	8	9	10
11	12	13	14	15	16	17
18	19	20	21	22	23	24
25	26	27	28	29	30	31
1	2	3	4	5	6	7

FEBRUARY

M	T	W	T	F	S	S
1	2	3	4	5	6	7
8	9	10	11	12	13	14
15	16	17	18	19	20	21
22	23	24	25	26	27	28
1	2	3	4	5	6	7
8	9	10	11	12	13	14

MARCH

M	T	W	T	F	S	S
1	2	3	4	5	6	7
8	9	10	11	12	13	14
15	16	17	18	19	20	21
22	23	24	25	26	27	28
29	30	31	1	2	3	4
5	6	7	8	9	10	11

APRIL

M	T	W	T	F	S	S
29	30	31	1	2	3	4
5	6	7	8	9	10	11
12	13	14	15	16	17	18
19	20	21	22	23	24	25
26	27	28	29	30	1	2
3	4	5	6	7	8	9

MAY

M	T	W	T	F	S	S
26	27	28	29	30	1	2
3	4	5	6	7	8	9
10	11	12	13	14	15	16
17	18	19	20	21	22	23
24	25	26	27	28	29	30
31	1	2	3	4	5	6

JUNE

M	T	W	T	F	S	S
31	1	2	3	4	5	6
7	8	9	10	11	12	13
14	15	16	17	18	19	20
21	22	23	24	25	26	27
28	29	30	1	2	3	4
5	6	7	8	9	10	11

JULY

M	T	W	T	F	S	S
28	29	30	1	2	3	4
5	6	7	8	9	10	11
12	13	14	15	16	17	18
19	20	21	22	23	24	25
26	27	28	29	30	31	1
2	3	4	5	6	7	8

AUGUST

M	T	W	T	F	S	S
26	27	28	29	30	31	1
2	3	4	5	6	7	8
9	10	11	12	13	14	15
16	17	18	19	20	21	22
23	24	25	26	27	28	29
30	31	1	2	3	4	5

SEPTEMBER

M	T	W	T	F	S	S
30	31	1	2	3	4	5
6	7	8	9	10	11	12
13	14	15	16	17	18	19
20	21	22	23	24	25	26
27	28	29	30	1	2	3
4	5	6	7	8	9	10

OCTOBER

M	T	W	T	F	S	S
27	28	29	30	1	2	3
4	5	6	7	8	9	10
11	12	13	14	15	16	17
18	19	20	21	22	23	24
25	26	27	28	29	30	31
1	2	3	4	5	6	7

NOVEMBER

M	T	W	T	F	S	S
1	2	3	4	5	6	7
8	9	10	11	12	13	14
15	16	17	18	19	20	21
22	23	24	25	26	27	28
29	30	1	2	3	4	5
6	7	8	9	10	11	12

DECEMBER

M	T	W	T	F	S	S
29	30	1	2	3	4	5
6	7	8	9	10	11	12
13	14	15	16	17	18	19
20	21	22	23	24	25	26
27	28	29	30	31	1	2
3	4	5	6	7	8	9

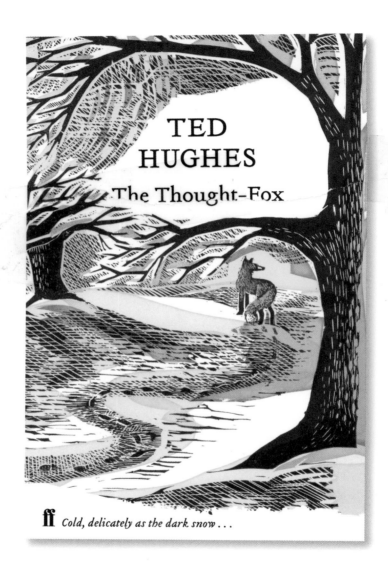

TED HUGHES

The Thought-Fox

ff *Cold, delicately as the dark snow . . .*

30 Monday

31 Tuesday

1 Wednesday　NEW YEAR'S DAY (UK, IRL, AUS, ZA, NZ, CAN)

2 Thursday　2ND JANUARY HOLIDAY (SCT)
DAY AFTER NEW YEAR'S DAY (NZ)

3 Friday

4 Saturday　　　　5 Sunday

from When the Egg Meets the Whisk

Late on summer Saturdays,
This is what the verger sweeps:
Ombre moons, pistachios, ash,
Hearts cut from upcycled maps,
Scalloped bits of Austen novels,
Hot pushed handfuls of white petals.

This is what the broom releases:
Acetate of Camel Lights,
Pheromones of human fear,
Public libraries' unwashed armpits,
Sweet sweat like a pound cake rising,
Modern roses' nothingness.

This is how things mix together,
Matter's endgame of fawn-dun,
The inevitable greyish
Persil makes its money from.

So when something singular
Comes along, it is a miracle:
Hail tap-dances down the tarmac,
Skittering in its silver shoes.

Three Poems (2018)

6 Monday

7 Tuesday

8 Wednesday

9 Thursday

10 Friday

11 Saturday   12 Sunday

The January Birds

The birds in Nunhead Cemetery begin
Before I've flicked a switch, turned on the gas.
There must be some advantage to the light

I tell myself, viewing my slackened chin
Mirrored in the rain-dark window glass,
While from the graveyard's trees, the birds begin.

An image from a dream survives the night,
Some dreck my head refuses to encompass.
There must be some advantage to the light.

You are you I mouth to my shadow skin,
Though you are me, assuming weight and mass —
While from the graveyard's trees, the birds begin:

Thrush, blackbird, finch — then rooks take fright
At a skip-truck and protest, cawing en masse.
There must be some advantage to the light

Or birds would need the gift of second sight
To sing *Another year will come to pass!*
The birds in Nunhead Cemetery begin,
There must be some advantage to the light.

Maurice
Riordan
The Holy
Land

The Holy Land (2007)

13 Monday

14 Tuesday

15 Wednesday

16 Thursday

17 Friday

18 Saturday

19 Sunday

Up in the Morning Early

Up in the morning's no for me,
　Up in the morning early;
When a' the hills are cover'd wi' snaw,
　I'm sure it's winter fairly.

Cold blaws the wind frae east to west,
　The drift is driving sairly;
Sae loud and shrill's I hear the blast,
　I'm sure it's winter fairly.

The birds sit chittering in the thorn,
　A' day they fare but sparely;
And lang's the night frae e'en to morn,
　I'm sure it's winter fairly.

Up in the morning's no for me,
　Up in the morning early;
When a' the hills are cover'd wi' snaw,
　I'm sure it's winter fairly.

20 Monday

21 Tuesday

22 Wednesday

23 Thursday

24 Friday

25 **Saturday** BURNS NIGHT

26 **Sunday** AUSTRALIA DAY (AUS)

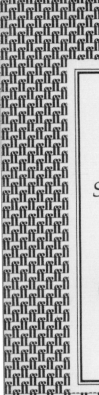

ANNE
RIDLER

*New and
Selected Poems*

27 Monday   AUSTRALIA DAY HOLIDAY (AUS)

28 Tuesday

29 Wednesday

30 Thursday

31 Friday

1 Saturday   2 Sunday

February Afternoon

Men heard this roar of parleying starlings, saw,
   A thousand years ago even as now,
   Black rooks with white gulls following the plough
So that the first are last until a caw
Commands that last are first again, – a law
   Which was of old when one, like me, dreamed how
   A thousand years might dust lie on his brow
Yet thus would birds do between hedge and shaw.

Time swims before me, making as a day
   A thousand years, while the broad ploughland oak
   Roars mill-like and men strike and bear the stroke
     Of war as ever, audacious or resigned,
And God still sits aloft in the array
     That we have wrought him, stone-deaf and stone-blind.

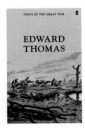

Edward Thomas: Selected Poems (2011)

3 Monday

4 Tuesday

5 Wednesday

6 Thursday   WAITANGI DAY (NZ)

7 Friday

8 Saturday   9 Sunday

Aura

Listen to me	little water
I called you up	believing something
would arise	in me believing
I could make	you reappear
on my way	to the cemetery
every face was	luminous
as if they knew	something about
the dark	I think you
were in us all	reminding me not
to despair or if	despairing know
that we did not	lose each other
either side	of the calamity
we fused	you went inside
& I could not	see you
but afterwards	afterwards
I could see	underwater I
could see in the dark	I could see
with my eyes closed	I could see past
the shimmer that	separates the living
& the dead I knew	there was nothing
no separation	it was just
aura the most	remarkable
sadness &	if only I would
keep looking	I would see you

Stranger, Baby (2017)

10 Monday

11 Tuesday

12 Wednesday

13 Thursday

14 Friday   VALENTINE'S DAY

15 Saturday   16 Sunday

The Conway Stewart

'Medium', 14-carat nib,
Three gold bands in the clip-on screw-top,
In the mottled barrel a spatulate, thin

Pump-action lever
The shopkeeper
Demonstrated,

The nib uncapped,
Treating it to its first deep snorkel
In a newly opened ink-bottle,

Guttery, snottery,
Letting it rest then at an angle
To ingest,

Giving us time
To look together and away
From our parting, due that evening,

To my longhand
'Dear'
To them, next day.

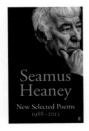

New Selected Poems 1988–2013 (2014)

17 Monday

18 Tuesday

19 Wednesday

20 Thursday

21 Friday

22 Saturday

23 Sunday

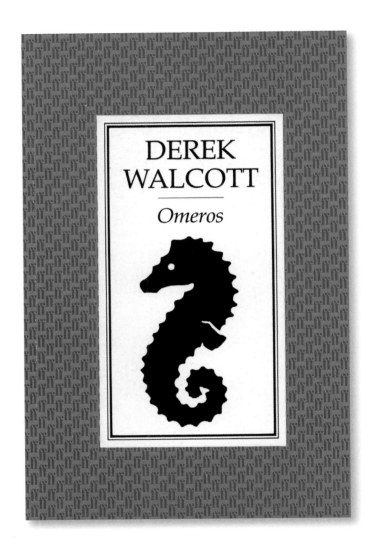

DEREK
WALCOTT

Omeros

24 Monday

25 Tuesday

26 Wednesday

27 Thursday

28 Friday

29 Saturday

1 Sunday ST DAVID'S DAY

The Missel-Thrush's Nest

In early March, before the lark
Dare start, beside the huge oak tree,
Close fixed agen the powdered bark,
The mavis' nest I often see;
And mark, as wont, the bits of wool
Hang round about its early bed;
She lays six eggs in colours dull,
Blotched thick with spots of burning red.

2 Monday

3 Tuesday

4 Wednesday

5 Thursday

6 Friday

7 Saturday

8 Sunday

March morning unlike others

Blue haze. Bees hanging in air at the hive-mouth.
Crawling in prone stupor of sun
On the hive-lip. Snowdrops. Two buzzards,
Still-wings, each
Magnetized to the other,
Float orbits.
Cattle standing warm. Lit, happy stillness.
A raven, under the hill,
Coughing among bare oaks.
Aircraft, elated, splitting blue.
Leisure to stand. The knee-deep mud at the trough
Stiffening. Lambs freed to be foolish.

The earth invalid, dropsied, bruised, wheeled
Out into the sun,
After the frightful operation.
She lies back, wounds undressed to the sun,
To be healed,
Sheltered from the sneapy chill creeping North wind,
Leans back, eyes closed, exhausted, smiling
Into the sun. Perhaps dozing a little.
While we sit, and smile, and wait, and know
She is not going to die.

15 March 1974

Ted
Hughes
Moortown
Diary

Moortown Diary (1979)

9 Monday

10 Tuesday

11 Wednesday

12 Thursday

13 Friday

14 Saturday   15 Sunday

To the Evening Star

Thou fair-hair'd angel of the evening,
Now, whilst the sun rests on the mountains, light
Thy bright torch of love; thy radiant crown
Put on, and smile upon our evening bed!
Smile on our loves, and while thou drawest the
Blue curtains of the sky, scatter thy silver dew
On every flower that shuts its sweet eyes
In timely sleep. Let thy west wind sleep on
The lake; speak silence with thy glimmering eyes,
And wash the dusk with silver. Soon, full soon,
Dost thou withdraw; then the wolf rages wide,
And the lion glares thro' the dun forest:
The fleeces of our flocks are cover'd with
Thy sacred dew: protect them with thine influence.

101 Sonnets (2012)

16 Monday

17 Tuesday ST PATRICK'S DAY HOLIDAY (IRL, NI)

18 Wednesday

19 Thursday

20 Friday

21 Saturday HUMAN RIGHTS DAY (ZA)

22 Sunday

American Poetry

AN INTRODUCTORY
ANTHOLOGY,
EDITED WITH AN
INTRODUCTION BY
DONALD HALL

23 Monday

24 Tuesday

25 Wednesday

26 Thursday

27 Friday

28 Saturday

29 Sunday

Discretion

i.m. Wisława Szymborska (1923–2012)

Children already
learn and recite your lines,
too young to believe you
were a real person, one of them, once.

When you die, there's a small stir
in the books pages here
like the splash
in hidden water

when some tiny, shy creature
has slipped away.
A phalanx of spears,
reeds keep us off.

Doves (2017)

30 Monday

31 Tuesday

1 Wednesday

2 Thursday

3 Friday

4 Saturday

5 Sunday

The Everlasting Monday

Thou shalt have an everlasting
Monday and stand in the moon.

The moon's man stands in his shell,
Bent under a bundle
Of sticks. The light falls chalk and cold
Upon our bedspread.
His teeth are chattering among the leprous
Peaks and craters of those extinct volcanoes.

He also against black frost
Would pick sticks, would not rest
Until his own lit room outshone
Sunday's ghost of sun;
Now works his hell of Mondays in the moon's ball,
Fireless, seven chill seas chained to his ankle.

Sylvia Plath: Poems Chosen by Carol Ann Duffy (2012)

6 Monday

7 Tuesday

8 Wednesday

9 Thursday

10 Friday   GOOD FRIDAY (UK, AUS, ZA, NZ, CAN)

11 Saturday   EASTER (HOLY)   12 Sunday   EASTER SUNDAY
                 SATURDAY

Vertue

Sweet day, so cool, so calm, so bright,
The bridall of the earth and skie:
The dew shall weep thy fall to night;
                For thou must die.

Sweet rose, whose hue angrie and brave
Bids the rash gazer wipe his eye:
Thy root is ever in its grave,
                And thou must die.

Sweet spring, full of sweet dayes and roses,
A box where sweets compacted lie;
My musick shows ye have your closes,
                And all must die.

Onely a sweet and vertuous soul,
Like season'd timber, never gives;
But though the whole world turn to coal,
                Then chiefly lives.

POET TO POET *George Herbert: Poems Selected by Jo Shapcott* (2006)

13 Monday   EASTER MONDAY (UK NOT SCT, IRL, AUS, NZ)
             FAMILY DAY (ZA)

14 Tuesday

15 Wednesday

16 Thursday

17 Friday

18 Saturday   19 Sunday

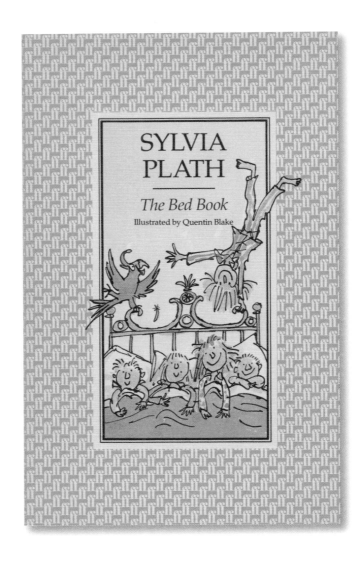

20 Monday

21 Tuesday

22 Wednesday

23 Thursday   ST GEORGE'S DAY

24 Friday

25 Saturday   ANZAC DAY   26 Sunday

Down by the Salley Gardens

Down by the salley gardens my love and I did meet;
She passed the salley gardens with little snow-white feet.
She bid me take love easy, as the leaves grow on the tree;
But I, being young and foolish, with her would not agree.

In a field by the river my love and I did stand,
And on my leaning shoulder she laid her snow-white hand.
She bid me take life easy, as the grass grows on the weirs;
But I was young and foolish, and now am full of tears.

POETRY PLEASE (2013)

27 **Monday**   ANZAC DAY OBSERVED (AUS, NZ)
FREEDOM DAY (ZA)

28 Tuesday

29 Wednesday

30 Thursday

1 **Friday**   WORKERS' DAY (ZA)

2 Saturday

3 Sunday

SOPHIE COLLINS

Untitled

The village is always on fire.
Men stay away from the kitchens,
take up in outhouses with concrete floors,
while the women — soot in their hair —
initiate the flames into their small routines.

Sophie
Collins
Who Is
Mary Sue?

Who Is Mary Sue? (2018)

4 **Monday** EARLY MAY BANK HOLIDAY (UK)
MAY DAY (IRL)

5 Tuesday

6 Wednesday

7 Thursday

8 Friday

9 Saturday 10 Sunday

To My Heart, On Sunday

Thank you, my heart:
you don't dawdle, you keep going
with no flattery or reward,
just from inborn diligence.

You get seventy credits a minute.
Each of your systoles
shoves a little boat
to open sea
to sail around the world.

Thank you, my heart:
time after time
you pluck me, separate even in sleep,
out of the whole.

You make sure I don't dream my dreams
up to that final flight,
no wings required.

Thank you, my heart:
I woke up again
and even though it's Sunday,
the day of rest,
the usual preholiday rush
continues underneath my ribs.

Poems New and Collected 1957–1997 (1998)

11 Monday

12 Tuesday

13 Wednesday

14 Thursday

15 Friday

16 Saturday   17 Sunday

Pomes
Penyeach
James
Joyce

MAY 2020

18 Monday

19 Tuesday

20 Wednesday

21 Thursday

22 Friday

23 Saturday   24 Sunday

The Windhover

I caught this morning morning's minion, kingdom
  of daylight's dauphin, dapple-dawn-drawn Falcon, in his
    riding
  Of the rolling level underneath him steady air, and striding
High there, how he rung upon the rein of a wimpling wing
In his ecstasy! then off, off forth on swing,
  As a skate's heel sweeps smooth on a bow-bend: the hurl
    and gliding
  Rebuffed the big wind. My heart in hiding
Stirred for a bird, – the achieve of, the mastery of the thing!

Brute beauty and valour and act, oh, air, pride, plume, here
  Buckle! AND the fire that breaks from thee then, a billion
Times told lovelier, more dangerous. O my chevalier!

  No wonder of it: shéer plód makes plough down sillion
Shine, and blue-bleak embers, ah my dear,
  Fall, gall themselves, and gash gold-vermilion.

POET TO POET *Gerard Manley Hopkins: Poems Selected by John Stammers* (2012)

25 **Monday** SPRING BANK HOLIDAY (UK)

26 Tuesday

27 Wednesday

28 Thursday

29 Friday

30 Saturday   31 Sunday

Remember

Remember me when I am gone away,
   Gone far away into the silent land;
   When you can no more hold me by the hand,
Nor I half turn to go yet turning stay.
Remember me when no more day by day
   You tell me of our future that you planned:
   Only remember me; you understand
It will be late to counsel then or pray.
Yet if you should forget me for a while
   And afterwards remember, do not grieve:
   For if the darkness and corruption leave
   A vestige of the thoughts that once I had,
Better by far you should forget and smile
   Than that you should remember and be sad.

Sounds Good: 101 Poems to be Heard (1998)

1 Monday   JUNE BANK HOLIDAY (IRL)
           QUEEN'S BIRTHDAY HOLIDAY (NZ)

2 Tuesday

3 Wednesday

4 Thursday

5 Friday

6 Saturday   7 Sunday

You

The Electric Telegraph has saved us.
— DONALD MCLEOD, Commissioner, British Punjab

———— *1857. Stop. Send help. Stop. Mutiny to come . . .*
Nine decades shy of the bomb
dropping from the sky on Dad's education
which stopped at the age of *maybe seven.*
'Mutiny', or 'Rebellion'? Words and words
only. And neither his. Or theirs. My dad
in his wordless sleep

would kick Mum in hers. Or in the heat
of the moment, ablaze, lit with drink, he'd
say *After you their Tempest planes bombed my school*
or *You are always king of divide and rule*
or *My hands are tied. My tongue can't make good fist
of speech like you. Because of you.* You. The English
second-person plural. Or singular

who arrived in the world in 1947.
A teacher. Five foot tall. I'd hear her.   *Stop*

Us (2018)

8 Monday

9 Tuesday

10 Wednesday

11 Thursday

12 Friday

13 Saturday   14 Sunday

A Local Habitation

Norman Nicholson

15 Monday

16 Tuesday   YOUTH DAY (ZA)

17 Wednesday

18 Thursday

19 Friday

20 Saturday   21 Sunday

Cowslips and Larks

I hear it said yon land is poor,
In spite of those rich cowslips there —
And all the singing larks it shoots
To heaven from the cowslips' roots.
But I, with eyes that beauty find,
And music ever in my mind,
Feed my thoughts well upon that grass
Which starves the horse, the ox, and ass.
So here I stand, two miles to come
To Shapwick and my ten-days-home,
Taking my summer's joy, although
The distant clouds are dark and low,
And comes a storm that, fierce and strong,
Has brought the Mendip Hills along:
Those hills that, when the light is there,
Are many a sunny mile from here.

POETRY PLEASE *The Seasons* (2015)

22 Monday

---

23 Tuesday

---

24 Wednesday

---

25 Thursday

---

26 Friday

---

27 Saturday   28 Sunday

'Still to be neat, still to be dressed'

Still to be neat, still to be dressed,
As you were going to a feast;
Still to be powdered, still perfumed:
Lady, it is to be presumed,
Though art's hid causes are not found,
All is not sweet, all is not sound.

Give me a look, give me a face,
That makes simplicity a grace;
Robes loosely flowing, hair as free:
Such sweet neglect more taketh me
Than all th' adulteries of art;
They strike mine eyes, but not my heart.

Sounds Good: 101 Poems to be Heard (1998)

29 Monday

30 Tuesday

1 Wednesday   CANADA DAY (CAN)

2 Thursday

3 Friday

4 Saturday   5 Sunday

grave weather

His wife's graveside service
was just barely finished,
when there was a massive
clap of thunder, followed
by a tremendous bolt of
lightning, accompanied by
a sunflower's pollination.

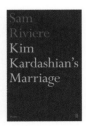

Kim Kardashian's Marriage (2015)

6 Monday

7 Tuesday

8 Wednesday

9 Thursday

10 Friday

11 Saturday

12 Sunday   BATTLE OF THE BOYNE
HOLIDAY (NI)

Ishion
Hutchinson
House of
Lords and
Commons

Poetry

ff

13 Monday

14 Tuesday

15 Wednesday

16 Thursday

17 Friday

18 Saturday

19 Sunday

The Good Morrow

I'm not sure I remember what we did
before we LOVED. Were we gherkins bobbing
in our harmless jars, with vinegar and seeds?
Or were we stuffed in a tube of sleep for years?
Probably; but that kind of life is carbohydrate.
If I enjoyed anything then it was feeling FULL.

The rover is making dust-ladder tracks on Mars.
The Victorian sewers have been overhauled, widened.
And here we both are, up-and-dressed.
But it's initimidating isn't it
when cack-handed LOVE is at his console,
nuking all life beyond this tenuous room.
I'm going to rely heavily on you, out there.

Happiness (2015)

20 Monday

21 Tuesday

22 Wednesday

23 Thursday

24 Friday

25 Saturday   26 Sunday

Burnt Norton

iv

Time and the bell have buried the day,
The black cloud carries the sun away.
Will the sunflower turn to us, will the clematis
Stray down, bend to us; tendril and spray
Clutch and cling?
Chill
Fingers of yew be curled
Down on us? After the kingfisher's wing
Has answered light to light, and is silent, the light is still
At the still point of the turning world.

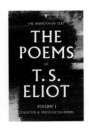

27 Monday

28 Tuesday

29 Wednesday

30 Thursday

31 Friday

1 Saturday   2 Sunday

Pebble

The pebble
is a perfect creature

equal to itself
mindful of its limits

filled exactly
with a pebbly meaning

with a scent which does not remind one of anything
does not frighten anything away does not arouse desire

its ardour and coldness
are just and full of dignity

I feel a heavy remorse
when I hold it in my hand
and its noble body
is permeated by false warmth

 — Pebbles cannot be tamed
 to the end they will look at us
 with a calm and very clear eye

The Faber Book of Modern European Poetry (1992)

3 **Monday** AUGUST BANK HOLIDAY (IRL)

4 Tuesday

5 Wednesday

6 Thursday

7 Friday

8 Saturday

9 **Sunday** NATIONAL WOMEN'S DAY (ZA)

T.S. ELIOT

POEMS
Written in Early Youth

10 Monday

11 Tuesday

12 Wednesday

13 Thursday

14 Friday

15 Saturday   16 Sunday

Summer Dawn

Pray but one prayer for me 'twixt thy closed lips,
Think but one thought of me up in the stars.
   The summer night waneth, the morning light slips,
Faint & grey 'twixt the leaves of the aspen, betwixt the
   cloud-bars,
That are patiently waiting there for the dawn:
   Patient and colourless, though Heaven's gold
Waits to float through them along with the sun.
Far out in the meadows, above the young corn,
   The heavy elms wait, and restless and cold
The uneasy wind rises; the roses are dun;
Through the long twilight they pray for the dawn.
Round the lone house in the midst of the corn.
Speak but one word to me over the corn,
Over the tender, bow'd locks of the corn.

17 Monday

18 Tuesday

19 Wednesday

20 Thursday

21 Friday

22 Saturday

23 Sunday

Connolly's Bookshop

It will come to all of us. First close off
the upstairs, blockading it with banks
of books you're not allowed to see, or presumed
to be interested in seeing. Next the shelves
on the back wall where philosophy was.
In due course the languages will go, until
bit by bit you're marooned in the middle
on your high stool amongst the books that show
why books are out of date, why you must move
with the times and be careful what you stock,
defiant Crusoe at the centre of your island.

Bernard
O'Donoghue
The Seasons
of Cullen
Church

The Seasons of Cullen Church (2016)

24 Monday

25 Tuesday

26 Wednesday

27 Thursday

28 Friday

29 Saturday   30 Sunday

WILLIAM SHAKESPEARE

'Like as the waves make towards the pebbled shore'

Like as the waves make towards the pebbled shore,
So do our minutes hasten to their end;
Each changing place with that which goes before,
In sequent toil all forwards do contend.
Nativity, once in the main of light,
Crawls to maturity, wherewith being crown'd,
Crooked eclipses 'gainst his glory fight,
And Time that gave doth now his gift confound.
Time doth transfix the flourish set on youth
And delves the parallels in beauty's brow,
Feeds on the rarities of nature's truth,
And nothing stands but for his scythe to mow:
    And yet to times in hope my verse shall stand,
    Praising thy worth, despite his cruel hand.

Sounds Good: 101 Poems to be Heard (1998)

3 1   **Monday**   SUMMER BANK HOLIDAY (UK)

1   Tuesday

2   Wednesday

3   Thursday

4   Friday

5   Saturday   6   Sunday

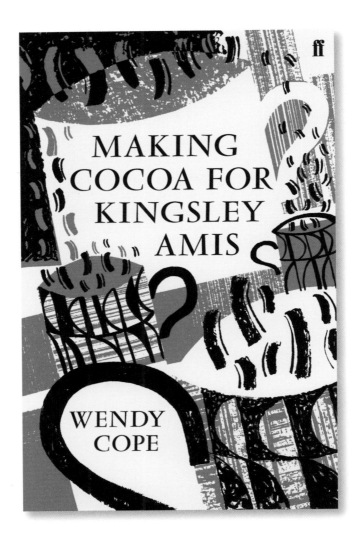

MAKING
COCOA FOR
KINGSLEY
AMIS

WENDY
COPE

7 **Monday**   LABOUR DAY (CAN)

8 **Tuesday**

9 **Wednesday**

10 **Thursday**

11 **Friday**

12 **Saturday**   13 **Sunday**

Sonnet to Sleep

O soft embalmer of the still midnight,
    Shutting, with careful fingers and benign,
Our gloom-pleas'd eyes, embower'd from the light,
    Enshaded in forgetfulness divine:
O soothest Sleep! if so it please thee, close
    In midst of this thine hymn my willing eyes,
Or wait the 'Amen,' ere thy poppy throws
    Around my bed its lulling charities.
Then save me, or the passed day will shine
Upon my pillow, breeding many woes, —
    Save me from curious Conscience, that still lords
Its strength for darkness, burrowing like a mole;
    Turn the key deftly in the oiled wards,
And seal the hushed Casket of my Soul.

POETRY PLEASE (2013)

14 Monday

15 Tuesday

16 Wednesday

17 Thursday

18 Friday

19 Saturday

20 Sunday

Lacan Appeals to the Patient

Since you remain reluctant, let us imagine
that one's selfhood is a work of art — a maquette
in clay, as may be, and each life event
enacted by the sculptor. In he creeps
to the damp-room on his crepe-soled shoes
again and again. In time the work proceeds
via a series of flukes and inspirations:
the sculptor warms to his task; the clay responds
with little sucking sounds until it is wrapped
and laid for next time on its wooden shelf.
Nothing is done in that place that is not reparable.
Beyond the clayey dark your helpmeet is waiting.
And though his feet in the stiff grass ache with cold
he keeps, while he can, his faith; his night lamp lifted.

Girlhood (2019)

21 Monday

22 Tuesday

23 Wednesday

24 Thursday   HERITAGE DAY (ZA)

25 Friday

26 Saturday   27 Sunday

Nothing To Be Said

For nations vague as weed,
For nomads among stones,
Small-statured cross-faced tribes
And cobble-close families
In mill-towns on dark mornings
Life is slow dying.

So are their separate ways
Of building, benediction,
Measuring love and money
Ways of slow dying.
The day spent hunting pig
Or holding a garden-party,

Hours giving evidence
Or birth, advance
On death equally slowly.
And saying so to some
Means nothing; others it leaves
Nothing to be said.

The Complete Poems (2012)

28 Monday

29 Tuesday

30 Wednesday

1 Thursday

2 Friday

3 Saturday

4 Sunday

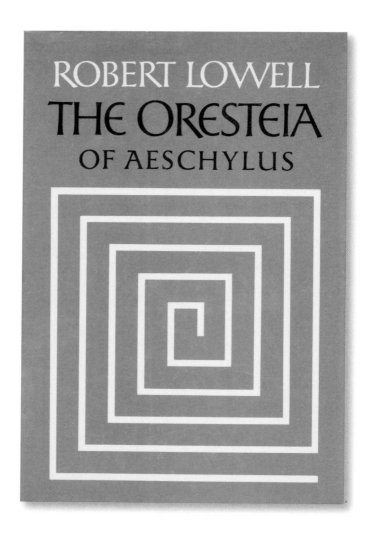

5 Monday

6 Tuesday

7 Wednesday

8 Thursday

9 Friday

10 Saturday

11 Sunday

Sudden Light

I have been here before,
　　But when or how I cannot tell:
I know the grass beyond the door,
　　The sweet keen smell,
The sighing sound, the lights around the shore.

You have been mine before,
　　How long ago I may not know:
But just when at that swallow's soar
　　Your neck turned so,
Some veil did fall – I knew it all of yore.

Has this been thus before?
　　And shall not thus time's eddying flight
Still with our lives our love restore
　　In death's despite,
And day and night yield one delight once more?

12 **Monday** THANKSGIVING DAY (CAN)

13 Tuesday

14 Wednesday

15 Thursday

16 Friday

17 Saturday   18 Sunday

On His Blindness

When I consider how my light is spent
Ere half my days, in this dark world and wide,
And that one talent which is death to hide
Lodged with me useless, though my soul more bent

To serve therewith my Maker, and present
My true account, lest He returning chide, –
Doth God exact day-labour, light denied?
I fondly ask: – But Patience, to prevent

That murmur, soon replies; God doth not need
Either man's work, or His own gifts: who best
Bear His mild yoke, they serve Him best: His state

Is kingly; thousands at His bidding speed
And post o'er land and ocean without rest: –
They also serve who only stand and wait.

19 Monday

20 Tuesday

21 Wednesday

22 Thursday

23 Friday

24 Saturday

25 Sunday

'The world is too much with us'

The world is too much with us; late and soon,
Getting and spending, we lay waste our powers:
Little we see in Nature that is ours;
We have given our hearts away, a sordid boon!
This Sea that bares her bosom to the moon;
The winds that will be howling at all hours,
And are up-gathered now like sleeping flowers;
For this, for everything, we are out of tune;
It moves us not. — Great God! I'd rather be
A Pagan suckled in a creed outworn;
So might I, standing on this pleasant lea,
Have glimpses that would make me less forlorn;
Have sight of Proteus rising from the sea;
Or hear old Triton blow his wreathèd horn.

Sounds Good: 101 Poems to be Heard (1998)

26 **Monday**   OCTOBER BANK HOLIDAY (IRL)
LABOUR DAY (NZ)

27 Tuesday

28 Wednesday

29 Thursday

30 Friday

31 **Saturday**   HALLOWEEN   I **Sunday**

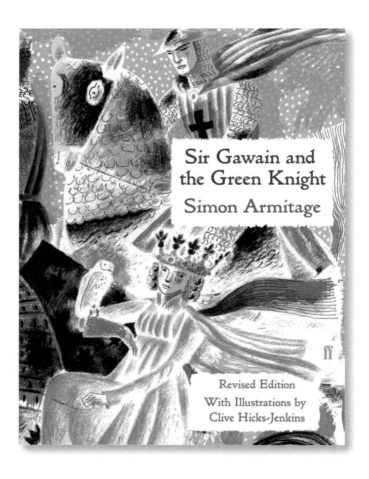

Sir Gawain and
the Green Knight

Simon Armitage

Revised Edition
With Illustrations by
Clive Hicks-Jenkins

2 Monday

3 Tuesday

4 Wednesday

5 Thursday

6 Friday

7 Saturday

8 Sunday   REMEMBRANCE SUNDAY

A. E. HOUSMAN

Epitaph on an Army of Mercenaries

These, in the day when heaven was falling,
    The hour when earth's foundations fled,
Followed their mercenary calling
    And took their wages and are dead.

Their shoulders held the sky suspended;
    They stood, and earth's foundations stay;
What God abandoned, these defended,
    And saved the sum of things for pay.

First World War Poems (2004)

9   Monday

10   Tuesday

11   Wednesday   REMEMBRANCE DAY (CAN)

12   Thursday

13   Friday

14   Saturday   15   Sunday

'The Day grew small, surrounded tight'

The Day grew small, surrounded tight
By early, stooping Night –
The Afternoon in Evening deep
Its Yellow shortness dropt –
The Winds went out their martial ways
The Leaves obtained excuse –
November hung his Granite Hat
Upon a nail of Plush –

POET TO POET *Emily Dickinson: Poems Selected by Ted Hughes* (1968)

16 Monday

17 Tuesday

18 Wednesday

19 Thursday

20 Friday

21 Saturday

22 Sunday

Snow

The room was suddenly rich and the great bay-window was
Spawning snow and pink roses against it
Soundlessly collateral and incompatible:
World is suddener than we fancy it.

World is crazier and more of it than we think,
Incorrigibly plural. I peel and portion
A tangerine and spit the pips and feel
The drunkenness of things being various.

And the fire flames with a bubbling sound for world
Is more spiteful and gay than one supposes —
On the tongue on the eyes on the ears in the palms of one's hands —
There is more than glass between the snow and the huge roses.

POETRY PLEASE *The Seasons* (2015)

2 3   Monday

2 4   Tuesday

2 5   Wednesday

2 6   Thursday

2 7   Friday

2 8   Saturday   2 9   Sunday

Nick
Laird
Feel
Free

Poetry

ff

30 **Monday**   ST ANDREW'S DAY HOLIDAY (SCT)

1 Tuesday

2 Wednesday

3 Thursday

4 Friday

5 Saturday   6 Sunday

To the Author of a Sonnet

beginning "'Sad is my verse," you say, "and yet no tear'"

Thy verse is 'sad' enough, no doubt:
    A devilish deal more sad than witty!
Why we should weep I can't find out,
    Unless for *thee* we weep in pity.

Yet there is one I pity more;
    And much, alas! I think he needs it;
For he, I'm sure, will suffer sore,
    Who, to his own misfortune, reads it.

Thy rhymes, without the aid of magic,
    May *once* be read – but never after:
Yet their effect's by no means tragic,
    Although by far too dull for laughter.

But would you make our bosoms bleed,
    And of no common pang complain –
If you would make us weep indeed,
    Tell us, you'll read them o'er again.

The Funny Side: 101 Humorous Poems (1998)

7 Monday

8 Tuesday

9 Wednesday

10 Thursday

11 Friday

12 Saturday

13 Sunday

A Robin

Ghost-grey the fall of night,
   Ice-bound the lane,
Lone in the dying light
   Flits he again;
Lurking where shadows steal,
Perched in his coat of blood,
Man's homestead at his heel,
   Death-still the wood.

Odd restless child; it's dark;
   All wings are flown
But this one wizard's — hark!
   Stone clapped on stone!
Changeling and solitary,
Secret and sharp and small,
Flits he from tree to tree,
   Calling on all.

POETRY PLEASE *The Seasons* (2015)

14 Monday

15 Tuesday

16 Wednesday   DAY OF RECONCILIATION (ZA)

17 Thursday

18 Friday

19 Saturday   20 Sunday

The Oxen

Christmas Eve, and twelve of the clock.
　'Now they are all on their knees,'
An elder said as we sat in a flock
　By the embers in hearthside ease.

We pictured the meek mild creatures where
　They dwelt in their strawy pen,
Nor did it occur to one of us there
　To doubt they were kneeling then.

So fair a fancy few would weave
　In these years! Yet, I feel,
If someone said on Christmas Eve,
　'Come; see the oxen kneel

'In the lonely barton by yonder coomb
　Our childhood used to know,'
I should go with him in the gloom,
　Hoping it might be so.

21 Monday

22 Tuesday

23 Wednesday

24 Thursday   CHRISTMAS EVE

25 Friday   CHRISTMAS DAY (UK, IRL, AUS, ZA, NZ, CAN)

26 Saturday   BOXING DAY (UK, AUS, NZ)   27 Sunday
ST STEPHEN'S DAY (IRL)
DAY OF GOODWILL (ZA)

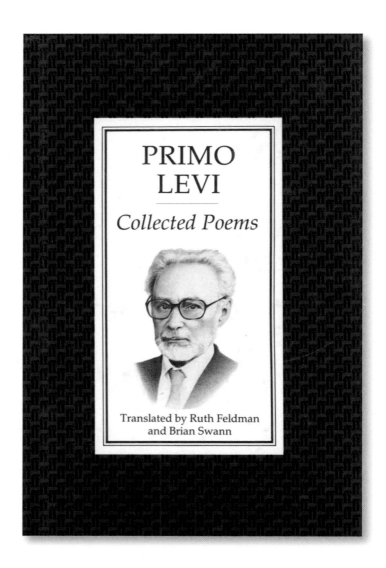

PRIMO
LEVI

Collected Poems

Translated by Ruth Feldman
and Brian Swann

28 Monday   BOXING DAY HOLIDAY (UK, AUS, NZ)

29 Tuesday

30 Wednesday

31 Thursday   NEW YEAR'S EVE

1 Friday   NEW YEAR'S DAY (UK, IRL, AUS, ZA, NZ, CAN)

2 Saturday   2ND JANUARY
HOLIDAY (SCT)
DAY AFTER NEW
YEAR'S DAY (NZ)

3 Sunday

A Brief Chronology of Faber's Poetry Publishing

1925 Geoffrey Faber acquires an interest in The Scientific Press and renames the firm Faber and Gwyer. ¶ The poet/bank clerk T. S. Eliot is recruited. 'What will impress my directors favourably is the sense that in you we have found a man who combines literary gifts with business instincts.' – Geoffrey Faber to T. S. Eliot ¶ Eliot brought with him *The Criterion*, the quarterly periodical he had been editing since 1922. (*The Waste Land* had appeared in its first issue, brilliantly establishing its reputation.) He continued to edit it from the Faber offices until it closed in 1939. Though unprofitable, it was hugely influential, introducing early work by Auden, Empson and Spender, among others, and promoting many notable European writers, including Proust and Valéry. ¶ Publication of T. S. Eliot's *Poems, 1909–1925*, which included *The Waste Land* and a new sequence, *The Hollow Men*. ¶

1927 From 1927 to 1931 Faber publishes a series of illustrated pamphlets known as *The Ariel Poems* containing unpublished poems by an eminent poet (Thomas Hardy, W. B. Yeats, Harold Monro, Edith Sitwell and Edmund Blunden, to name but a few) along with an illustration, usually in colour, by a leading contemporary artist (including Eric Gill, Eric Ravilious, Paul Nash and Graham Sutherland). ¶

1928 Faber and Gwyer announce the *Selected Poems of Ezra Pound*, with an introduction and notes by Eliot. ¶

1929 Geoffrey Faber buys out Lady Gwyer and oversees the birth of the Faber and Faber imprint. Legend has it that Walter de la Mare, the father of Faber director Richard de la Mare, suggested the euphonious repetition: another Faber in the company name 'because you can't have too much of a good thing'. ¶

1930 W. H. Auden becomes a Faber poet with a collection entitled simply *Poems*. ¶ Eliot publishes *Ash Wednesday*. ¶

1933 Stephen Spender becomes a Faber poet with his first collection *Poems*, a companion piece to Auden's 1930 work of the same name. ¶ The first British edition of James Joyce's *Pomes Penyeach* is published. ¶

1935 The American poet Marianne Moore publishes with Faber. 'Miss Moore's poems form part of a small body of durable poetry written in our time.' – T. S. Eliot ¶ Louis MacNeice becomes a Faber poet. 'The most original Irish poet of his generation.' – Faber catalogue 1935 ¶

1936 The hugely influential *Faber Book of Modern Verse* (edited by Michael Roberts) is published. ¶

1937 *In Parenthesis* by David Jones is published. 'This is an epic of war. But it is like no other war-book because for the first time that experience has been reduced to "a shape in words." The impression still remains that this book is one of the most remarkable literary achievements of our time.' – *Times Literary Supplement* ¶ W. H. Auden is awarded the Queen's Gold Medal for Poetry. ¶

1939 T. S. Eliot's *Old Possum's Book of Practical Cats* is published with a book jacket illustrated by the author. Originally called *Pollicle Dogs and Jellicle Cats*, the poems were written for his five godchildren. The eldest of these was Geoffrey Faber's son Tom – himself much later a director of Faber and Faber. ¶

1944 Walter de la Mare's *Peacock Pie* is published with illustrations by Edward Ardizzone. ¶ Philip Larkin's first novel, *A Girl in Winter*, is published. 'A young man with an exceptionally clear sense of what, as a writer, he means to do.' – *Times Literary Supplement* ¶

1948 T. S. Eliot wins the Nobel Prize in Literature. ¶

1949 Ezra Pound's *Pisan Cantos* is published. 'The most incomprehensible passages are often more stimulating than much comprehensibility which passes for poetry today.' – *Times Literary Supplement* ¶

1954 *The Ariel Poems* are revived with a new set of pamphlets by W. H. Auden, Stephen Spender, Louis MacNeice, T. S. Eliot, Walter de la Mare, Cecil Day Lewis and Roy Campbell. The artists include Edward Ardizzone, Edward Bawden, Michael Ayrton and John Piper. ¶

1957 Ted Hughes comes to Faber with *The Hawk in the Rain*. ¶ Siegfried Sassoon receives the Queen's Gold Medal for Poetry. ¶

1959 Robert Lowell's collection *Life Studies* is published. ¶

1960 Saint-John Perse wins the Nobel Prize in Literature. ¶

1961 Geoffrey Faber dies. ¶ Ted Hughes's first collection of children's poems, *Meet My Folks*, is published. ¶

1963 The Geoffrey Faber Memorial Prize is established as an annual prize awarded in alternating years to a single volume of poetry or fiction by a Commonwealth author under forty. ¶

1964 Philip Larkin's *The Whitsun Weddings* is published. ¶

1965 T. S. Eliot dies. ¶ Sylvia Plath's posthumous collection, *Ariel*, is published. 'Her extraordinary achievement, poised as she was between volatile emotional state and the edge of the precipice.' – Frieda Hughes ¶ Philip Larkin is awarded the Queen's Gold Medal for Poetry. ¶

1966 Seamus Heaney comes to Faber with *Death of a Naturalist*. ¶ Sylvia Plath's novel *The Bell Jar* is published by Faber. ¶

1968 Ted Hughes's *The Iron Man* is published. ¶

1971 Stephen Spender is awarded the Queen's Gold Medal for Poetry. ¶

1973 Paul Muldoon comes to Faber with his first collection, *New Weather*. ¶

1974 Ted Hughes receives the Queen's Gold Medal for Poetry. ¶

1977 Tom Paulin comes to Faber with his first collection, *A State of Justice*. ¶ Norman Nicholson receives the Queen's Gold Medal for Poetry. ¶

1980 Czesław Miłosz wins the Nobel Prize in Literature. ¶

1981 *Cats*, the Andrew Lloyd Webber musical based on *Old Possum's Book of Practical Cats*, opens in London. ¶

1984 *Rich*, a collection by Faber's own poetry editor, Craig Raine, is published. 'Puts us in touch with life as unexpectedly and joyfully as early Pasternak.' – John Bayley ¶ Ted Hughes becomes Poet Laureate. ¶

1985 Douglas Dunn's collection *Elegies* is the Whitbread Book of the Year. ¶

1986 Vikram Seth's *The Golden Gate* is published. ¶

1987 Seamus Heaney's *The Haw Lantern* wins the Whitbread Poetry Award. ¶

1988 Derek Walcott is awarded the Queen's Gold Medal for Poetry. ¶

1992 Derek Walcott wins the Nobel Prize in Literature. ¶ Thom Gunn's collection *The Man with the Night Sweats* wins the Forward Poetry Prize for Best Collection, while Simon Armitage's *Kid* wins Best First Collection. ¶

1993 Andrew Motion wins the Whitbread Biography Award for his book on Philip Larkin. ¶ Don Paterson's *Nil Nil* wins the Forward Poetry Prize for Best First Collection. ¶

1994 Paul Muldoon wins the T. S. Eliot Prize for *The Annals of Chile*. ¶ Alice Oswald wins an Eric Gregory Award. ¶

1995 Seamus Heaney wins the Nobel Prize in Literature. ¶

1996 Wisława Szymborska wins the Nobel Prize in Literature. ¶ Seamus Heaney's *The Spirit Level* wins the Whitbread Poetry Award. 'Touched by a sense of wonder.' – Blake Morrison ¶

1997 Don Paterson wins the T. S. Eliot Prize for *God's Gift to Women*. ¶ Lavinia Greenlaw wins the Forward Prize for Best Single Poem for 'A World Where News Travelled Slowly'. ¶ Ted Hughes's *Tales from Ovid* is the Whitbread Book of the Year. 'A breathtaking book.' – John Carey ¶

1998 Ted Hughes wins the Whitbread Book of the Year for the second time running with *Birthday Letters*, which also wins the T. S. Eliot Prize. 'Language like lava, its molten turmoils hardening into jagged shapes.' – John Carey ¶ Ted Hughes is awarded the Order of Merit. ¶ Christopher Logue receives the Wilfred Owen Poetry Award. ¶

1999 Seamus Heaney's *Beowulf* wins the Whitbread Book of the Year Award. '[Heaney is the] one living poet who can rightly claim to be Beowulf's heir.' – *New York Times* ¶ A memorial service for Ted Hughes is held at Westminster Abbey. In his speech Seamus Heaney calls Hughes 'a guardian spirit of the land and language'. ¶ Hugo Williams wins the T. S. Eliot Prize for his collection *Billy's Rain*. ¶ Andrew Motion is appointed Poet Laureate. ¶

2000 Seamus Heaney receives the Wilfred Owen Poetry Award. ¶

2002 Alice Oswald wins the T. S. Eliot Prize for Poetry for her collection *Dart*. ¶

2003 Paul Muldoon is awarded the Pulitzer Prize for Poetry for *Moy Sand and Gravel*. *Landing Light* by Don Paterson wins the Whitbread Poetry Award. ¶

2004 August Kleinzahler receives the International Griffin Poetry Prize for *The Strange Hours Travellers Keep*. ¶ Hugo Williams is awarded the Queen's Gold Medal for Poetry. ¶

2005 David Harsent wins the Forward Prize for Best Collection for *Legion*. ¶ Harold Pinter receives the Wilfred Owen Poetry Award. ¶ Charles Simic receives the International Griffin Poetry Prize for *Selected Poems 1963–2003*. ¶ Nick Laird wins an Eric Gregory Award. ¶

2006 Christopher Logue wins the Whitbread Poetry Award for *Cold Calls*. ¶ The Geoffrey Faber Memorial Prize is awarded to Alice Oswald for *Woods Etc.* ¶ Seamus Heaney wins the T. S. Eliot Prize for *District and Circle*. ¶

2007 Tony Harrison is awarded the Wilfred Owen Poetry Award. ¶ Daljit Nagra wins the Forward Prize for Best First Collection for *Look We Have Coming to Dover!* ¶ James Fenton receives the Queen's Gold Medal for Poetry. ¶

2008 Daljit Nagra wins the South Bank Show / Arts Council Decibel Award. ¶ Mick Imlah's collection *The Lost Leader* wins the Forward Prize for Best Collection. ¶

2009 Carol Ann Duffy becomes Poet Laureate. ¶ Don Paterson's *Rain* wins the Forward Poetry Prize for Best Collection, while *The Striped World* by Emma Jones wins the Best First Collection Prize. ¶

2010 *The Song of Lunch* by Christopher Reid is shortlisted for the Ted Hughes Award for New Work in Poetry and he is awarded the Costa Poetry Award for *A Scattering.* ¶ The John Florio Prize for Italian Translation 2010 is awarded to Jamie McKendrick for *The Embrace.* ¶ Derek Walcott wins both the Warwick Prize and the T. S. Eliot Prize for Poetry for his collection *White Egrets.* ¶ *Rain* by Don Paterson is shortlisted for the Saltire Scottish Book of the Year. ¶ Tony Harrison is awarded the Prix Européen de Littérature. ¶ The Keats–Shelley Prize is awarded to Simon Armitage for his poem 'The Present'. ¶ The Forward Prize for Best Collection is awarded to Seamus Heaney for *Human Chain.* ¶ Also shortlisted for the Forward Prize for Best Collection are Lachlan Mackinnon for *Small Hours* and Jo Shapcott for *Of Mutability.* ¶ The Centre for Literacy in Primary Education (CLPE) Poetry Prize is awarded to Carol Ann Duffy for *New and Collected Poems for Children.* ¶ Alice Oswald wins the Ted Hughes Award for New Work in Poetry for *Weeds and Wild Flowers.* ¶ *The Striped World* by Emma Jones is shortlisted for the Adelaide Festival Poetry Award. ¶ The Queen's Gold Medal for Poetry is awarded to Don Paterson. ¶

2011 *Of Mutability* by Jo Shapcott is the Costa Book of the Year. ¶ *Human Chain* by Seamus Heaney and *Maggot* by Paul Muldoon are both shortlisted for the *Irish Times* Poetry Now Award. ¶ *Night* by David Harsent is shortlisted for the Forward Prize for Best Collection. ¶ 'Bees' by Jo Shapcott is shortlisted for the Forward Prize for Best Single Poem. ¶ A new digital edition of T. S. Eliot's *The Waste Land* for iPad is launched, bringing to life one of the most revolutionary poems of the last hundred years, illuminated by a wealth of interactive features. ¶ The Queen's Gold Medal for Poetry is awarded to Jo Shapcott. ¶ At Westminster Abbey a memorial is dedicated to Ted Hughes in Poets' Corner. ¶

2012 *The Death of King Arthur* by Simon Armitage is shortlisted for the T. S. Eliot Prize. ¶ *The World's Two Smallest Humans* by Julia Copus is shortlisted for the T. S. Eliot Prize and the Costa Poetry Award. ¶ David Harsent's collection *Night* wins the International Griffin Poetry Prize. ¶ *81 Austerities* by Sam Riviere wins the Felix Dennis Prize for Best First Collection, one of the Forward Prizes for Poetry. ¶ *Farmers Cross* by Bernard O'Donoghue is shortlisted for the *Irish Times* Poetry Now Award. ¶

2013 The Forward Prize for Best First Collection is awarded to Emily Berry for *Dear Boy.* ¶ Hugo Williams is shortlisted for the Forward Prize for Best Single

Poem for 'From the Dialysis Ward'. ¶ Alice Oswald is awarded the Warwick Prize for Writing for her collection *Memorial*, which also wins the Poetry Society's Corneliu M. Popescu Prize for poetry in translation. ¶ The Queen's Gold Medal for Poetry is awarded to Douglas Dunn. ¶ The shortlist for the T. S. Eliot Prize includes Daljit Nagra for *The Ramayana: A Retelling* and Maurice Riordan for *The Water Stealer*. ¶ *Pink Mist* by Owen Sheers wins the Hay Festival Medal for Poetry. ¶ In his eulogy for Seamus Heaney, Paul Muldoon says, 'We remember the beauty of Seamus Heaney – as a bard, and in his being.' In November the first official tribute evenings to Heaney are held at Harvard, then in New York, followed by events at the Royal Festival Hall in London, the Waterfront Hall, Belfast, and the Sheldonian, Oxford. ¶

2014 Maurice Riordan is shortlisted for the Pigott Poetry Prize for *The Water Stealer*. ¶ Hugo Williams is shortlisted for the Forward Prize for Best Collection for *I Knew the Bride*. ¶ Daljit Nagra is awarded the Society of Authors Travelling Scholarship. ¶ Nick Laird's *Go Giants* is shortlisted for the *Irish Times* Poetry Now Award. ¶ Emily Berry, Emma Jones and Daljit Nagra are announced as three of the Poetry Book Society's Next Generation Poets 2014. ¶ *Pink Mist* by Owen Sheers is named the Wales Book of the Year after winning the poetry category. ¶

2015 *Fire Songs* by David Harsent is awarded the T. S. Eliot Prize for Poetry. ¶ Alice Oswald wins the Ted Hughes Award for New Work for *Tithonus*, a poem and performance commissioned by London's Southbank Centre. ¶ *One Thousand Things Worth Knowing* by Paul Muldoon wins the Pigott Poetry Prize. ¶ Don Paterson is awarded the Neustadt International Prize for Literature. ¶ *Terror* by Toby Martinez de las Rivas is shortlisted for the Seamus Heaney Centre for Poetry's Prize for First Full Collection. ¶ Paul Muldoon's *One Thousand Things Worth Knowing* is shortlisted for the Forward Prize for Best Collection. ¶ James Fenton is awarded the Pen Pinter Prize. ¶ *40 Sonnets* by Don Paterson wins the Costa Poetry Award, and is short-listed for the T. S. Eliot Prize. ¶

2016 Don Paterson is shortlisted for the International Griffin Poetry Prize. ¶ *40 Sonnets* by Don Paterson is short-listed for the Saltire Society Literary Awards. ¶ *The Seasons of Cullen Church* by Bernard O'Donoghue is shortlisted for the T. S. Eliot Prize. ¶ Jack Underwood receives a Somerset Maugham Award. ¶ An excerpt from *Salt* by David Harsent is shortlisted for the Forward Prize for Best Single Poem. ¶

2017 *The Unaccompanied* by Simon Armitage, *Stranger, Baby* by Emily Berry and *The Noise of a Fly* by Douglas Dunn all receive Recommendations from the Poetry Book Society. They also give a Special Commendation to

Selected Poems of Thom Gunn, edited by Clive Wilmer. ¶ Simon Armitage receives the PEN Award for Poetry in Translation for *Pearl* ¶ Bernard O'Donoghue's collection *The Seasons of Cullen Church* is shortlisted for the Pigott Poetry Prize. ¶ Emily Berry's collection *Stranger, Baby* is shortlisted for the Forward Prize for Best Collection. ¶ Sam Riviere's collection *Kim Kardashian's Marriage* is shortlisted for the Ledbury Poetry Prize. ¶ Douglas Dunn's collection *The Noise of a Fly* is shortlisted for the T. S. Eliot Prize. ¶ Paul Muldoon is awarded the Queen's Gold Medal for Poetry. ¶

2018 Matthew Francis's collection *The Mabinogi* is shortlisted for the Ted Hughes Award and Welsh Book of the Year. ¶ Toby Martinez de las Rivas's collection *Black Sun* is shortlisted for the Forward Prize for Best Collection. ¶ Richard Scott's collection *Soho* is shortlisted for the Forward Prize for Best First Collection, the T. S. Eliot Prize and the Costa Poetry Award. ¶ Owen Sheers is the recipient of the Wilfred Owen Poetry Award for 2018. ¶ Daljit Nagra receives a Society of Authors Cholmondeley Award. ¶ Seamus Heaney's collection *100 Poems* is shortlisted for the 2018 Books Are My Bag Readers Awards, Poetry category. ¶ Nick Laird's collection *Feel Free* is shortlisted for the T. S. Eliot Prize. ¶ Zaffar Kunial's collection *Us* is shortlisted for the Costa Poetry Award and the T. S. Eliot Prize. ¶ Hannah Sullivan's collection *Three Poems* is shortlisted for the Roehampton Poetry Prize and the Costa Poetry Award, and goes on to win the T. S. Eliot Prize. ¶ Simon Armitage is awarded the Queen's Gold Medal for Poetry. ¶

Acknowledgements

Poetry

All poetry reprinted by permission of Faber & Faber alone unless otherwise stated.

Excerpt from 'When the Egg Meets the Whisk' taken from *Three Poems* © Hannah Sullivan ¶ 'January Birds' taken from *The Holy Land* © Maurice Riordan ¶ 'Aura' taken from *Stranger, Baby* © Emily Berry ¶ 'The Conway Stewart' taken from *New Selected Poems 1988–2013* © The Estate of Seamus Heaney ¶ 'March Morning Unlike Others' taken from *Collected Poems* © The Estate of Ted Hughes ¶ 'Discretion' taken from *Doves* © Lachlan Mackinnon ¶ 'The Everlasting Monday' taken from *Sylvia Plath: Poems Chosen by Carol Ann Duffy* © The Estate of Sylvia Plath ¶ 'Untitled' taken from *Who Is Mary Sue?* © Sophie Collins ¶ 'To My Heart, On

Picture credits

NOTES

FABER

MEMBERS

Become a Faber Member and discover the best in the arts and literature.

Sign up to the Faber Members programme and enjoy specially curated events, tailored discounts, and exclusive previews of our forthcoming publications from the best novelists, poets, playwrights, thinkers, musicians and artists.

ff

Join for free today at faber.co.uk/members